Audition Songs for
Professional Singers

Wise Publications
part of The Music Sales Group
London / New York / Paris / Sydney / Copenhagen / Berlin / Madrid / Tokyo

Published by
Wise Publications

Exclusive Distributors:
Music Sales Limited
8/9 Frith Street,
London W1D 3JB, England.
Music Sales Pty Limited
120 Rothschild Avenue,
Rosebery, NSW 2018,
Australia.

Order No. AM84708
ISBN 0-7119-2642-5
This book © Copyright 2004 by Wise Publications

Compiled by Lucy Holliday.
Printed and bound in Malta.

Your Guarantee of Quality
As publishers, we strive to produce every book
to the highest commercial standards.
This book has been carefully designed to minimise awkward
page turns and to make playing from it a real pleasure.
Particular care has been given to specifying acid-free,
neutral-sized paper made from pulps which have not been
elemental chlorine bleached. This pulp is from farmed sustainable
forests and was produced with special regard for the environment.
Throughout, the printing and binding have been planned to ensure a
sturdy, attractive publication which should give years of enjoyment.
If your copy fails to meet our high standards, please inform us and
we will gladly replace it.

www.musicsales.com

CD TRACKS

Disc 1

1. Angels (Williams/Chambers) EMI Virgin Music Limited/BMG Music Publishing Limited.
2. Can You Feel The Love Tonight (John/Rice) Warner/Chappell Artemis Music Limited.
3. Cry Me A River (Timberlake/Storch/Mosley) EMI Music Publishing Limited/
Warner/Chappell Music Limited/Zomba Music Publishers Limited.
4. Evergreen (Elofsson/Magnusson/Kreuger) BMG Music Publishing Limited/Good Ear Music/
Peermusic (UK) Limited/Warner/Chappell Music Limited.
5. (Everything I Do) I Do It For You (Adams/Lange/Kamen) Universal/MCA Music Limited/
Rondor Music (London) Limited/Zomba Music Publishers Limited.
6. Father And Son (Stevens) Sony/ATV Music Publishing (UK) Limited.
7. Flying Without Wings (Mac/Hector) Rokstone Music/Rondor Music (London) Limited.
8. Feel (Williams/Chambers) BMG Music Publishing Limited/EMI Music Publishing Limited.
9. Fields Of Gold (Sting) Steerpike Limited.
10. Have I Told You Lately (Morrison) Universal Music Publishing Limited.
11. Hey Jude (Lennon/McCartney) Sony/ATV Music Publishing (UK) Limited.
12. The Great Pretender (Ram) Peermusic (UK) Limited.
13. I Drove All Night (Kelly/Steinberg) Sony/ATV Music Publishing (UK) Limited.
14. I Can't Make You Love Me (Reid/Shamblin) BMG Music Publishing Limited/Rondor Music (London) Limited.

Disc 2

1. If Tomorrow Never Comes (Brooks/Blazy) Warner/Chappell North America/BMG Music Publishing Limited.
2. If You're Not The One (Bedingfield) Sony/ATV Music Publishing (UK) Limited.
3. In My Place (Berryman/Martin/Buckland/Champion) BMG Music Publishing Limited.
4. Leave Right Now (White) Universal Music Publishing Limited.
5. Jacky (Brel/Jouannest) Carlin Music Corporation.
6. Suspicious Minds (Zambon) Sony/ATV Music Publishing (UK) Limited.
7. Sail Away (Gray) Chrysalis Music Limited.
8. When You Say Nothing At All (Schlitz/Overstreet) Universal/MCA Music Limited/
BMG Music Publishing Limited/Screen Gems-EMI Music Limited.
9. Where The Streets Have No Name (U2) Blue Mountain Music Limited.
10. Wild Is The Wind (Washington/Tiomkin) Carlin Music Corporation/BMG Music Publishing Limited.
11. Wonderwall (Gallagher) Sony/ATV Music Publishing(UK) Limited.
12. Woman (Lennon) Lenono Music.
13. Writing To Reach You (Healy) Sony/ATV Music Publishing (UK) Limited.
14. You Do Something To Me (Weller) BMG Music Publishing Limited.

**To remove your CD from the plastic sleeve, lift the small
lip on the side to break the perforated flap.
Replace the disc after use for convenient storage.**

Disc 1

CD Track 1
Angels
Music: Page 6

In E major

CD Track 2
Can You Feel The Love Tonight
Music: Page 11

In B♭ major

CD Track 3
Cry Me A River
Music: Page 16

In G♯ minor

CD Track 4
Evergreen
Music: Page 22

In C major

CD Track 5
(Everything I Do) I Do It For You
Music: Page 27

In D major

CD Track 6
Father And Son
Music: Page 32

In G major

CD Track 7
Flying Without Wings
Music: Page 37

In A♭ major

CD Track 8
Feel
Music: Page 42

In D minor

CD Track 9
Fields Of Gold
Music: Page 50

In B minor

CD Track 10
Have I Told You Lately
Music: Page 56

In E major

CD Track 11
Hey Jude
Music: Page 60

In F major

CD Track 12
The Great Pretender
Music: Page 64

In G major

CD Track 13
I Drove All Night
Music: Page 71

In C major

CD Track 14
I Can't Make You Love Me
Music: Page 78

In G major

In B♭ major

CD Track 1
If Tomorrow Never Comes
Music: Page 84

In B♭ major

CD Track 2
If You're Not The One
Music: Page 88

In A major

CD Track 3
In My Place
Music: Page 94

In F♯ major

CD Track 4
Leave Right Now
Music: Page 98

In F♯ minor

CD Track 5
Jacky
Music: Page 104

In G major

CD Track 6
Suspicious Minds
Music: Page 111

In C minor

CD Track 7
Sail Away
Music: Page 116

In G major

CD Track 8
When You Say Nothing At All
Music: Page 122

In D major

CD Track 9
Where The Streets Have No Name
Music: Page 128

In A minor

CD Track 10
Wild Is The Wind
Music: Page 135

In F♯ minor

CD Track 11
Wonderwall
Music: Page 142

In E♭ major

CD Track 12
Woman
Music: Page 148

In F♯ minor

CD Track 13
Writing To Reach You
Music: Page 151

In E minor

CD Track 14
You Do Something To Me
Music: Page 156

Angels

Words & Music by Robbie Williams & Guy Chambers

9

Can You Feel The Love Tonight
(from Walt Disney Pictures' "The Lion King")

Words by Tim Rice
Music by Elton John

1.There's a calm___ sur - ren - der to the rush___ of day,___ when the heat___ of the roll - ing world___

can be turned___ a - way.___   An en - chant - ed mo - ment,

and it sees me through.___   It's e - nough___ for this rest - less war - rior

just to be___ with you.___   And can you feel___ the love___

___ to - night?___   It is where___ we are.___

There's a rhyme and rea-son to the wild out-doors when the heart of this star-crossed voy-ag-er

D.S al Coda

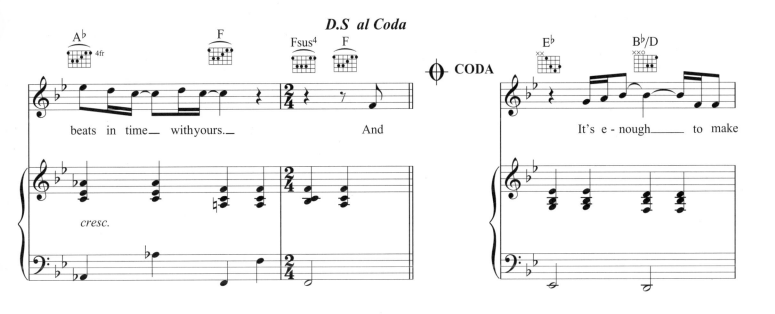

beats in time— with yours.— And

CODA

It's e-nough—— to make

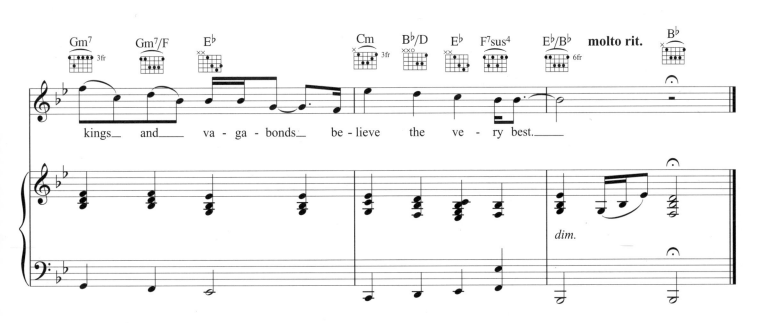

kings— and— va-ga-bonds— be-lieve the ve-ry best.——

Cry Me A River

Words & Music By Justin Timberlake, Scott Storch & Tim Mosley

Evergreen

Words & Music by Jorgen Elofsson, Per Magnusson & David Kreuger

that I need; 'cause you're more beau-ti-ful__ than I__ have ev-er seen,__

oh__ yeah. I'm gon-na take this night and make it ev-er green.__

We can make it last for ev - er more.__

Don't tell_ me_ that it feels like love.__ I'm gon-na take this

Verse 2:
Touch like an angel
Like velvet to my skin
And I wonder
I wonder why you wanna stay the night
What you're dreaming
What's behind.
Don't tell me, but it feels like love.

I'm gonna take this moment *etc.*

(Everything I Do) I Do It For You

Words by Bryan Adams & Robert John Lange
Music by Michael Kamen

no love___ like your love,___ and no___ oth - er could give___

more ___ love. There's no - where _____ un - less___ you're ___ there all the

time,_____ all the way,___ yeah._____

(Guitar solo)

Verse 2:
Look into your heart, you will find
There's nothin' there to hide.
Take me as I am, take my life
I would give it all, I would sacrifice
Don't tell me it's not worth fightin' for
I can't help it, there's nothin' I want more.
You know it's true, everything I do
I do it for you.

Father And Son

Words & Music by Cat Stevens

35

Flying Without Wings

Words & Music by Steve Mac & Wayne Hector

Ev-'ry-bo-dy's look-ing for that some - thing,— one thing that makes it all com-plete. You find it in— the stran-gest pla - ces,— pla-ces you nev - er knew it could be.— Some find it in— the face_ of

their child - ren,— some find it in— their lov - er's eyes.

Who can de - ny— the joy— it brings———— when you've found that spe - cial—

thing? You're fly - ing with - out wings. Some find it shar - ing ev - 'ry

morn - ing,———— some in their so - li - ta - ry lives.—
(Verse 3 see block lyric)

D.S. al Coda

40

Verse 3:
Well, for me it's waking up beside you
To watch the sun rise on your face
To know that I can say I love you
At any given time or place
It's little things that only I know
Those are the things that make you mine
And it's like flying without wings
'Cause you're my special thing
I'm flying without wings.

Feel

Words & Music By Robbie Williams & Guy Chambers

1. Come and hold my hand,
(2.)die

I wanna contact the living.
but I ain't keen on living either.

I just wan - na feel____ real__ love,__ feel the home that I live__ in.

I got too much love____ run-ning through my veins____ to go to waste.

____ I just want to feel____ real love_

____ and a life ev - er af - ter.____ There's a hole in my soul,

you can see it in my face, it's a real big place.____

Tr.6

Fields Of Gold

Words & Music by Sting

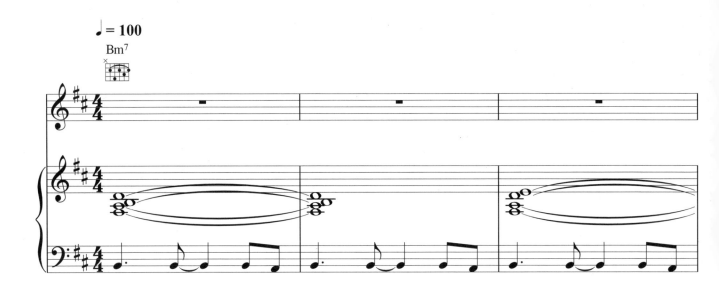

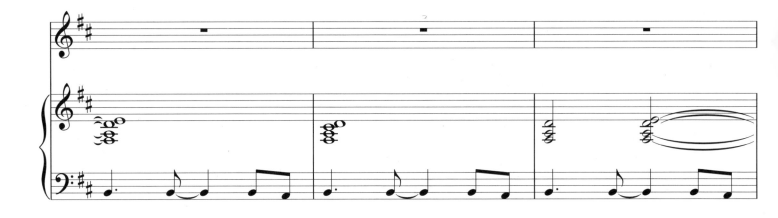

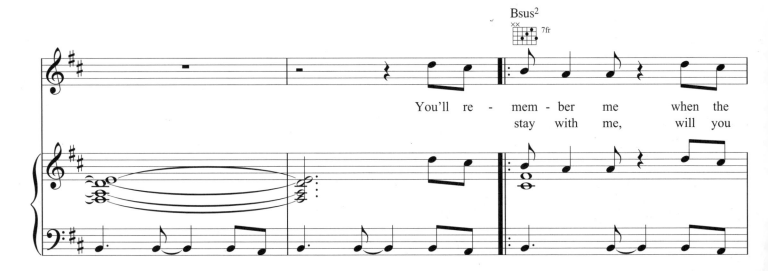

You'll re - mem - ber me when the
stay with me, when will you

west wind moves_ up - on the fields_ of bar - ley.   You'll for -
be my love_ a - mong the fields_ of bar - ley?   We'll for -

-get the sun in his jeal - ous sky as we walk in fields_ of gold.
-get the sun in his jeal - ous sky as we lie in fields_ of gold.

So she took her love for to gaze a - while_ up -
See the west wind move like a lov - er so_ up -

but I swear_ in the days still left we'll walk____ in fields_ of gold.

We'll____ walk in fields_ of gold.

Have I Told You Lately

Words & Music by Van Morrison

Hey Jude

Words & Music by John Lennon & Paul McCartney

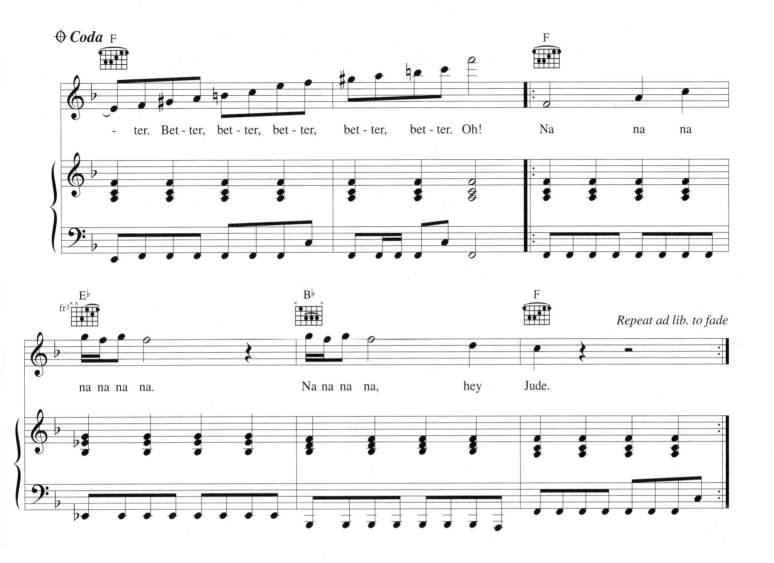

Verse 3:

Hey Jude, don't let me down

You have found her, now go and get her

Remember to let her into your heart

Then you can start to make it better

So let it out and let it in

Hey Jude, begin

You're waiting for someone to perform with

And don't you know that it's just you

Hey Jude, you'll do

The moment you need is on your shoulder

Na na na na na

Na na na na.

Verse 4:

Hey Jude, don't make it bad

Take a sad song and make it better

Remember to let her under your skin

Then you'll begin to make it better.

The Great Pretender

Words & Music by Buck Ram

clown._ I_____ seem_____ to

be what I'm not you_____ see._____ I'm

wear - ing_____ my heart like a crown. Pre -

- tend - ing that you're, pre - tend - ing that

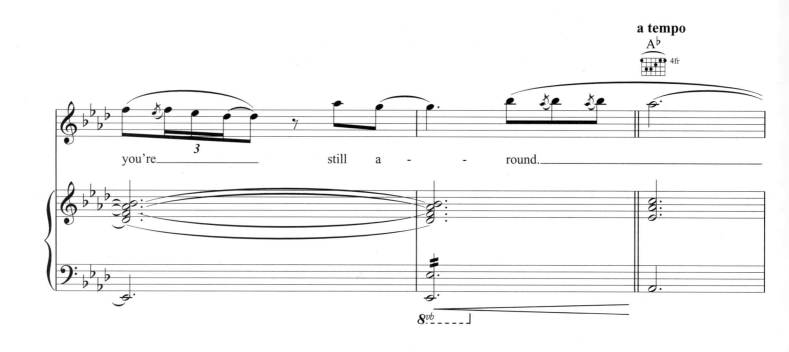

you're_____ still a - - round._____

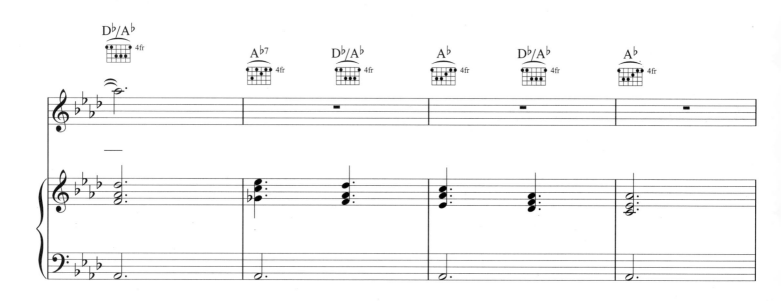

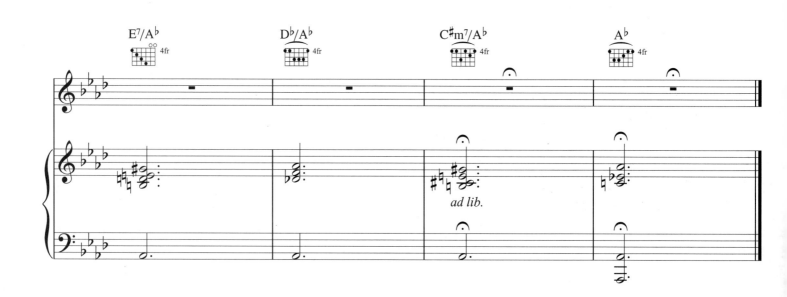

I Drove All Night

Words & Music by Tom Kelly & Billy Steinberg

1. I had to es-cape, the ci-ty was stick-y and cruel.
(Verse 2 see block lyric)

Verse 2:
What in this world keeps us from falling apart?
No matter where I go I hear the beating of our one heart
I think about you when the night is cold and dark
No-one can move me the way that you do
Nothing erases this feeling between me and you.

I drove all night *etc.*

I Can't Make You Love Me

Words & Music By Mike Reid & Allen Shamblin

turn down__ the bed,_____ turn down these voi - ces_____

in - side_____ my head._ Lay down with me,_____

tell me no__ lies,_____ just hold me close,____

don't pa - tron - ise.___ Don't_ pa - tron - ise_____

I feel___ the pow - er,___ but you won't,___ no,___ you___ won't. And I can't

make you___ love me if you___ don't.___

2. I'll close___ my___ eyes___ then I won't see___ the

If Tomorrow Never Comes

Words & Music by Garth Brooks & Kent Blazy

Verse 2:
'Cause I've lost loved ones in my life
Who never knew how much I loved them
Now I live with the regret
The natural feelings for them never were revealed
So I made a promise to myself
To say each day how much she means to me
And avoid that circumstance
Where there's no second chance
To tell her how I feel.

If tomorrow never comes *etc.*

If You're Not The One

Words & Music By Daniel Bedingfield

93

In My Place

Words & Music By Guy Berryman,
Chris Martin, Jon Buckland & Will Champion

1. In my place, in my____ place were lines that I____could-n't
(Verse 2 see block lyric)

Verse 2:
I was scared, I was scared
Tired and under-prepared
But I'll wait for it.
And if you go, if you go
And leave me down here on my own
Then I'll wait for you, yeah.

Yeah, how long must you wait *etc.*

Leave Right Now

Words & Music by Francis White

Jacky

Music by Jacques Brel
Original French Words by Gérard Jouannest
English Words by Mort Shuman

Come back.

D.S. al Coda

◊ **CODA**

Verse 2:
And if I joined the social whirl
Became procurer of young girls
Then I could have my own bordellos
My records would be number one
And I'd sell records by the ton
All sung by many other fellows.
My name would then be Handsome Jack
And I'd sell boats of opium
Whiskey that came from Twickenham
Authentic Queens and phoney virgins.
I'd have a bank on every finger
On every finger in every country
And every country ruled by me
I'd still know where I wanna be
Locked up inside my opium den
Surrounded by some China men
I'd sing the song that I sang then
About the time they called me "Jacky".

If I could be etc.

Verse 3:
Now tell me, wouldn't it be nice
That if one day in Paradise
I'd sing for all the ladies up there
And they would sing along with me
And we so happy there to be
'Cause down below is really nowhere.
My name would then be Jupiter
Then I would know where I was going
Become all-knowing
My beard so very long and flowing.
If I could play deaf, dumb and blind
Because I pitied all mankind
And broke my heart to make things right
I know that every single night
When my angelic work was through
The angels and the Devil too
Would sing my childhood song to me
About the time they called me "Jacky".

If I could be etc.

Suspicious Minds

Words & Music by Francis Zambon

1. We're caught in a trap,_
(Verses 2 & 3 see block lyrics)

I can't walk out,_____

be - cause I love__ you too__ much ba - by._____

when, ho - ney, you know I'll___ nev - er lie to you.___

Mm.___ Yeah, yeah.___

Tempo I

D.S. al Coda

Coda

when you don't be - lieve___ a word___ I say?___

Oh, don't you know I'm caught in a trap.___

114

Verse 2:

So if an old friend I know, drops by to say hello
Would I still see suspicion in your eyes?
Here we go again, asking where I've been
You can't see the tears are real I'm crying.

We can't go on together, with suspicious minds   *etc.*

Verse 3:

We're caught in a trap, I can't walk out
Because I love you too much, baby
Why can't you see what you're doing to me
When you don't believe a word I say?

We can't go on together, with suspicious minds   *etc.*

Sail Away

Words & Music by David Gray

Sail a - way— with me, ho-ney, I put my heart— in your hands.

Sail a - way— with me ho-ney now,—— now,—— now.—

and ev - 'ry - thing_____ I held_____ so dear_____

dis - ap - peared_____ with - out a trace._____

2. Though all the times_____ I tast - ed love,_____
(Verse 3 see block lyric)

nev - er knew_____ quite_____ what I had._____

Lit - tle dar - ling, if__ you hear__ me now,__

nev - er need-ed you so bad;__

spin-ning 'round_ in - side__ my head.__

2° only

Sail a - way_ with me, ho - ney, I put my heart_ in your hands.

Sail a - way — with me ho - ney now, — now, — now. —

sail a - way — with me; — what will be — will — be. —

1. I wan-na hold you — now, — now, — now. —

2. now, — now.

Sail — a - way — with me, ho - ney, I put my heart — in your hands.
(Choruses 5, 6 & 7 see block lyric)

Verse 3:
I've been talking drunken gibberish
Falling in and out of bars
Trying to get some explanation here
For the way some people are.
How did it ever come so far?

Chorus 5:
Sail away with me, honey
I put my heart in your hands.
It breaks me up if you pull me down, woh.
Sail away with me; what will be will be.
I wanna hold you now, now, now.

Chorus 6 & 7:
(Whistle)

When You Say Nothing At All

Words & Music by Don Schlitz & Paul Overstreet

me when-ev-er I fall.

You say it best when you say no-thing at all.

(You say it best when you say no-thing at all.)
(female vocals)

(You say it best when you say

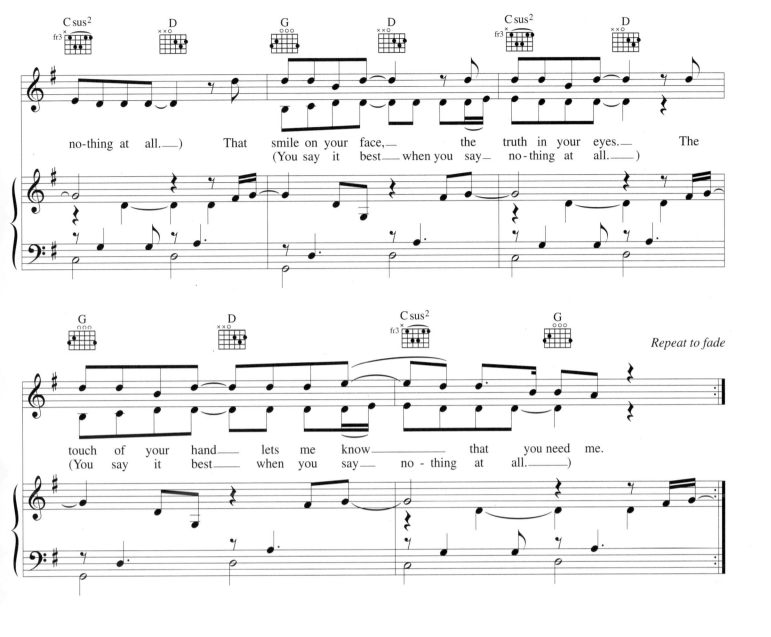

Verse 2:

All day long I can hear people talking out loud
But when you hold me you drown out the crowd
Try as they may they can never defy
What's been said between your heart and mine.

The smile on your face *etc.*

Where The Streets Have No Name

Words & Music by U2

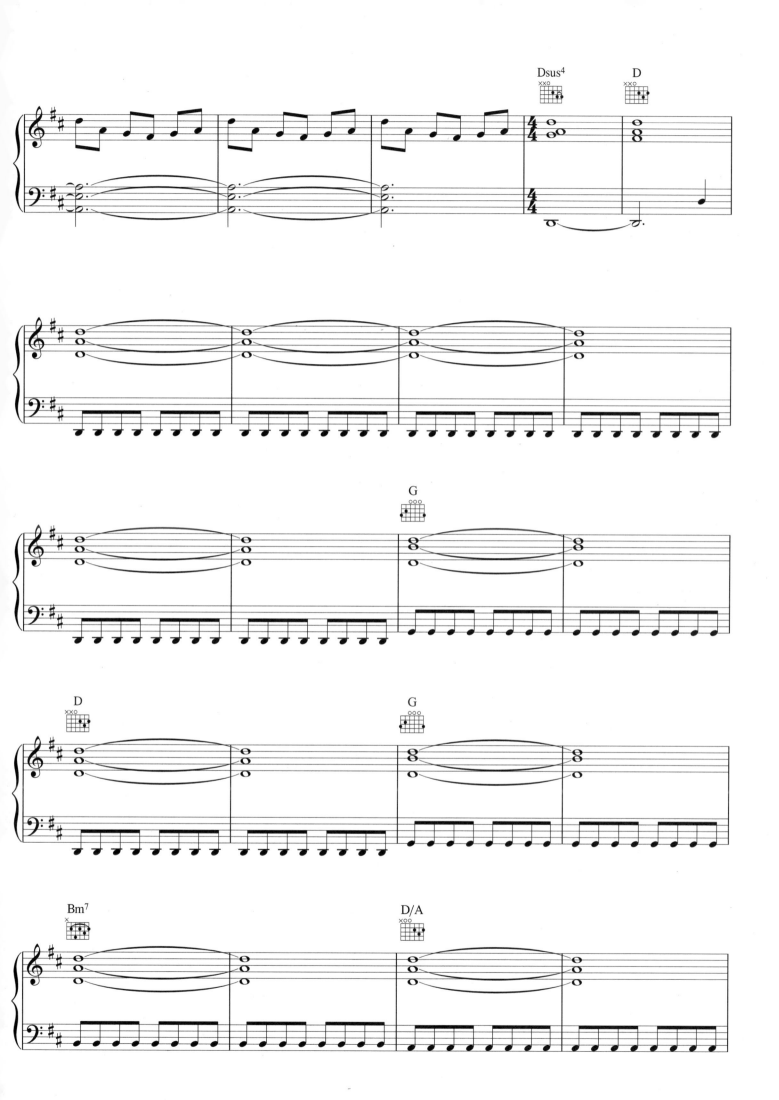

burn - ing down love, burn - ing down love.

And when I go there I go there with

you. It's all I can do.

3. The ci - ty's a

Wild Is The Wind

Words by Ned Washington
Music by Dimitri Tiomkin

and wild____ is the wind.____   Wild____ is the wind.

2. Give me more____ than one____ ca -
(Verse 3 & ℅ see block lyric)

- ress.   Sa - tis - fy____ this____

____ hun - - - gri - ness.____   Let the

of man - do - lins. You

kiss me,

with your kiss my life be - gins.

You're Spring to me,

Verse 3 & 𝄋:
Like the leaf clings to the tree
Oh, my darling cling to me
For we're like creatures of the wind
Wild is the wind
Wild is the wind.

You touch me *etc.*

Wonderwall

Words & Music by Noel Gallagher

1. To - day is gon - na be the day that they're gon - na throw it back to you,—

by now you should-'ve some - how re - al - ised what you got - ta do.—

I don't be - lieve_ that an - y - bo - dy feels the way I do_ a - bout you now._

2. Back - beat the word was on the street that the fire in your heart is out._
(Verse 3 see block lyric)

I'm sure you've heard it all be - fore but you nev - er real - ly had a doubt._

Verse 3:
Today was gonna be the day
But they'll never throw it back to you
By now you should've somehow
Realised what you're not to do
I don't believe that anybody
Feels the way I do
About you now.

And all the roads that lead you there were winding
And all the lights that light the way are blinding
There are many things that I would like to say to you
But I don't know how.

Woman

Words & Music by John Lennon

1. Wo - man, I can hard - ly ex - press my mixed e - mo - tions at my
2. Wo - man, I know you un - der - stand the lit - tle child in -

thought - less - ness. After all,— I'm for - ev - er in your debt.— And
- side the man. Please re - mem - ber, my life is in your hands.— And

woman, I will try to ex - press my in - ner feel - ings and
woman, hold me close to your heart. How - ev - er dis - tant, don't

thank - ful - ness for show - ing me the mean - ing of suc - cess.
keep us a - part. Af - ter all, it is writ - ten in the stars.

Ooh, well, well. Doo doo doo doo doo.

1.

Ooh. well, well. Doo doo doo doo doo.

doo doo.   Wo - man,   please let me ex - plain.__

I nev - er meant to cause you sor - row and pain.__ So let me tell you a -

-gain and a - gain and a - gain._____ I

love_____ you,   yeah, yeah,   now and for - ev - er.   I

Repeat to fade

Writing To Reach You

Words & Music by Fran Healy

You Do Something To Me

Words & Music by Paul Weller

won - der - ful
(Verse 3: instrumental to chorus)

then chase it all a - way,

mix - ing my e - mo -

- tions, that throws me back a - gain.

Hang - ing on the